Based on the best-selling keyboard method *by Kenneth Baker.*

8.95

THE COMPLE
KEYBOARD PL

C000100299

Pop Hits

This publication is not authorised for sale in
the United States of America and/or Canada

Wise Publications
part of The Music Sales Group
London/New York/Paris/Sydney/Copenhagen/Berlin/Madrid/Tokyo

Published by
Wise Publications
8/9 Frith Street, London W1D 3JB, UK

Exclusive Distributors:
Music Sales Limited
8/9 Frith Street, London W1D 3JB, UK.
Music Sales Pty Limited
120 Rothschild Avenue, Rosebery, NSW 2018, Australia.

This book © Copyright 2005 Wise Publications,
a division of Music Sales Limited.
Order No. AM983059
ISBN 1-84609-093-8

Unauthorised reproduction of any part of this publication by any
means including photocopying is an infringement of copyright.

Compiled by Nick Crispin.
Music arranged by Paul Honey.
Music processed by Paul Ewers Music Design.
Cover photograph courtesy of London Features International.
Printed in the United Kingdom by
Printwise (Haverhill) Limited, Haverhill, Suffolk.

Your Guarantee of Quality
As publishers, we strive to produce every book
to the highest commercial standards.
This book has been carefully designed to minimise awkward
page turns and to make playing from it a real pleasure.
Particular care has been given to specifying acid-free, neutral-sized paper
made from pulps which have not been elemental chlorine bleached.
This pulp is from farmed sustainable forests and was produced with special
regard for the environment. Throughout, the printing and binding have been
planned to ensure a sturdy, attractive publication which should give years of enjoyment.
If your copy fails to meet our high standards, please inform us and
we will gladly replace it.

www.musicsales.com

Master Chord Chart

C
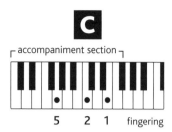

Cm
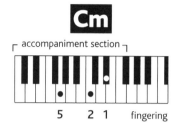

C 7
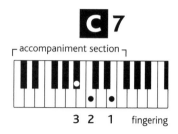

D♭(C#)
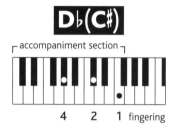

D♭(C#)m
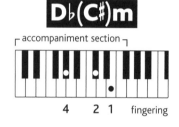

D♭(C#) 7
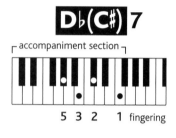

D
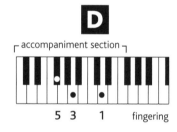

Dm
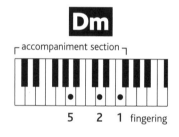

D 7
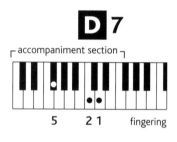

E♭(D#)
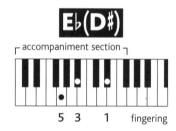

E♭(D#)m
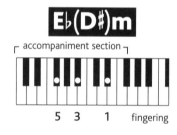

E♭(D#) 7
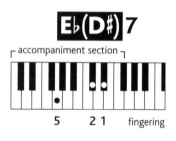

E
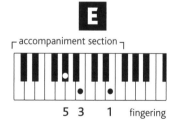

Em
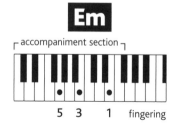

E 7
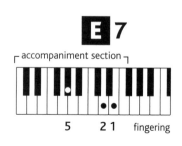

F
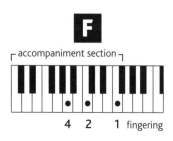

Fm
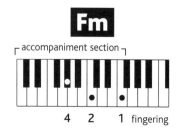

F 7
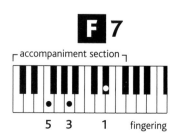

Master Chord Chart

G♭(F#)
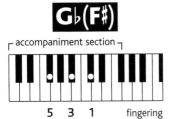
5   3   1   fingering

G♭(F#)m

5   3   1   fingering

G♭(F#)7

5   3   1   fingering

G
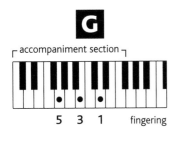
5   3   1   fingering

Gm
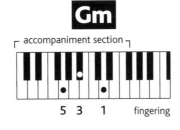
5   3   1   fingering

G7
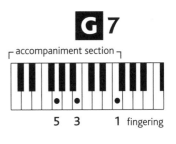
5   3   1   fingering

A♭(G#)
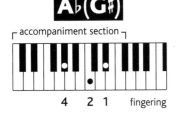
4   2   1   fingering

A♭(G#)m
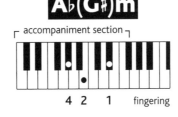
4   2   1   fingering

A♭(G#)7
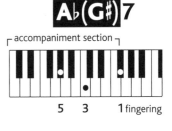
5   3   1 fingering

A
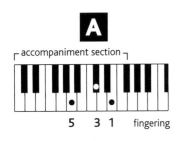
5   3   1   fingering

Am
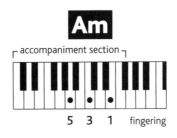
5   3   1   fingering

A7
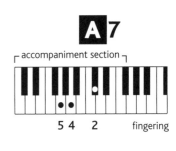
5   4   2   fingering

B♭
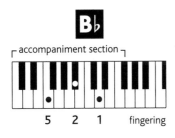
5   2   1   fingering

B♭m
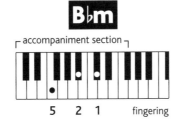
5   2   1   fingering

B♭7
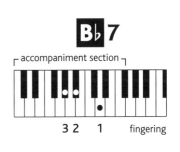
3 2   1   fingering

B
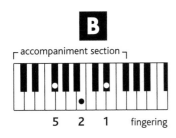
5   2   1   fingering

Bm
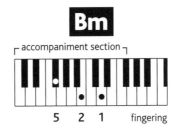
5   2   1   fingering

B7
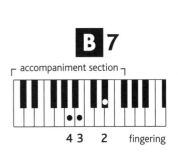
4 3   2   fingering

5

Beautiful

Christina Aguilera

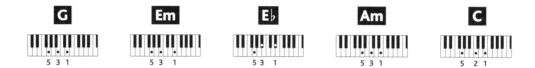

Voice: **Clarinet**
Rhythm: **8 beat ballad**
Tempo: ♩ = 74

Moderately

Ev - 'ry day is so won - der - ful, then sud - den -

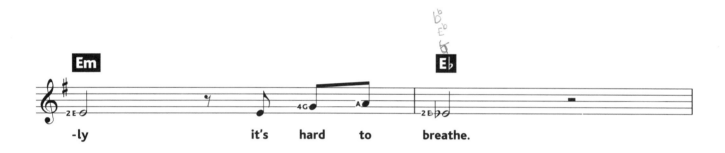

-ly it's hard to breathe.

Now and then I get in - se - cure from all the

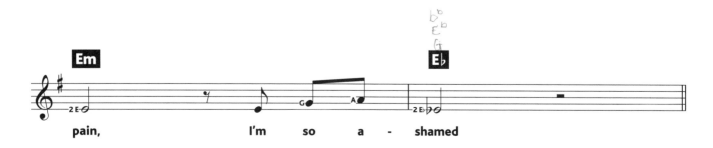

pain, I'm so a - shamed

Words & Music by Linda Perry

© Copyright 2003 Famous Music Publishing Limited.
All Rights Reserved. International Copyright Secured.

I am beau-ti-ful____ no mat-ter what they say.

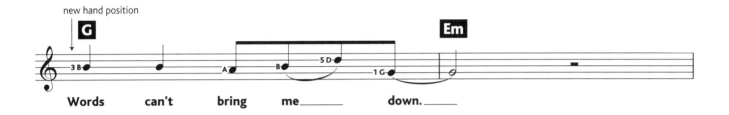

new hand position

Words can't bring me____ down.____

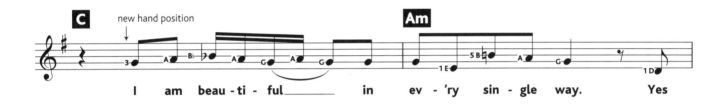

new hand position

I am beau-ti-ful_____ in ev-'ry sin-gle way. Yes

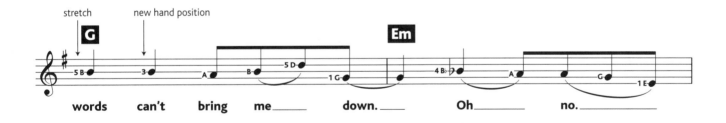

stretch   new hand position

words can't bring me____ down.____ Oh____ no.____

1.   2.

So don't you bring me down to - day.   - day.

Born To Try

Delta Goodrem

Voice: **Clarinet**
Rhythm: **8 beat ballad**
Tempo: ♩ = **70**

Quite Slow

Do - ing ev - 'ry - thing that I be - lieve in,

go - ing by the rules that I've been taught. _____

More un - der - stand - ing of what's a - round me, _____

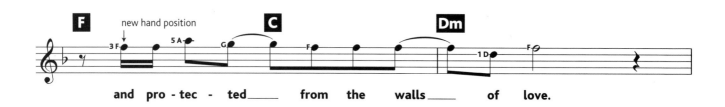

and pro - tec - ted _____ from the walls _____ of love.

Words & Music by Delta Goodrem & Audius Mtawarira

© Copyright 2003 Sony Music Publishing Australia PTY.
Sony/ATV Music Publishing (UK) Limited.
All Rights Reserved. International Copyright Secured.

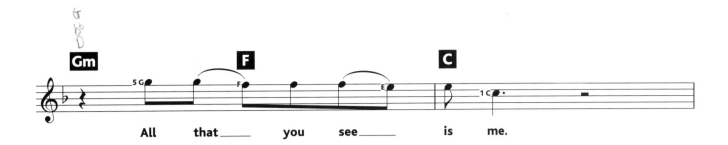

All that_____ you see_____ is me.

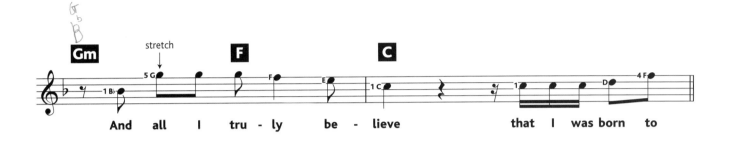

And all I tru - ly be - lieve that I was born to

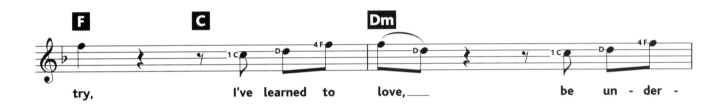

try, I've learned to love,_____ be un - der -

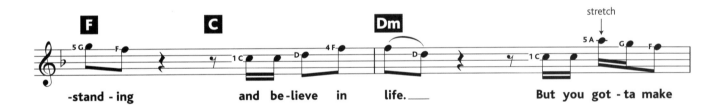

-stand - ing and be - lieve in life._____ But you got - ta make

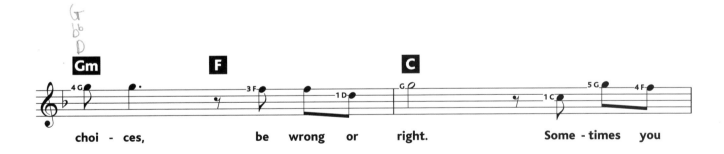

choi - ces, be wrong or right. Some - times you

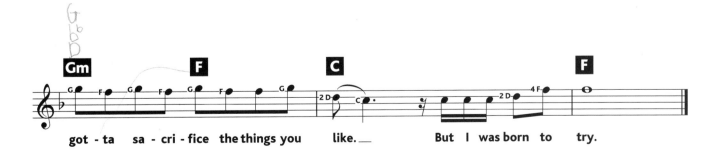

got - ta sa - cri - fice the things you like.__ But I was born to try.

9.

Breathe In

Lucie Silvas

Voice: **Piano**
Rhythm: **Rock**
Tempo: ♩ = 132

Bright Tempo

I feel I'm drag-ging you down a one way street, I

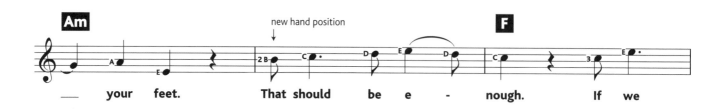

don't know which way's up, and all I ask of you is stay on

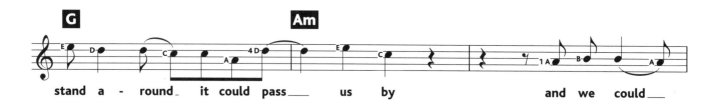

your feet. That should be e-nough. If we

stand a-round it could pass us by and we could

Words & Music by Michael Peden, Lucie Silvas, Judie Tzuke & Graham Kearns
© Copyright 2004 Globel Talent Publishing Limited (33.33%)/Chrysalis Music Limited (25%)/
Universal Music Publishing Limited (35%)/Copyright Control (6.67%).
All Rights Reserved. International Copyright Secured.

give up now, nev - er ev - en try.___

To breathe in life and breathe out___ like to -

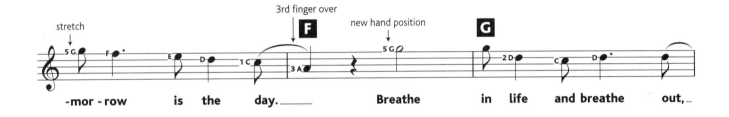

-mor - row is the day.___ Breathe in life and breathe out,___

___ and it's not so long to wait.___ Breathe

in life and breathe out,___ wipe the dust from your sweet

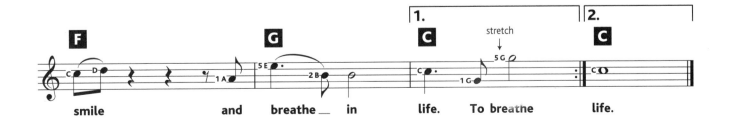

smile and breathe___ in life. To breathe life.

California

Phantom Planet

Voice: **Clarinet**
Rhythm: **8 beat ballad**
Synchro start: **On**
Tempo: ♩ = **70**

Quite Slow

We've been on the run, driv-ing in the sun, look-ing out for num-ber one, Ca - li -
On the ste-re - o, lis-ten as we go, no-thing's gon-na stop me now, Ca - li -

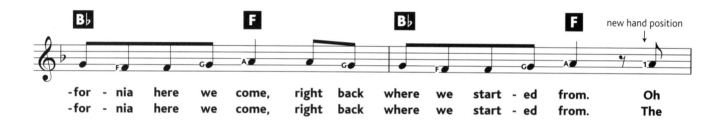

-for - nia here we come, right back where we start - ed from. Oh
-for - nia here we come, right back where we start - ed from. The

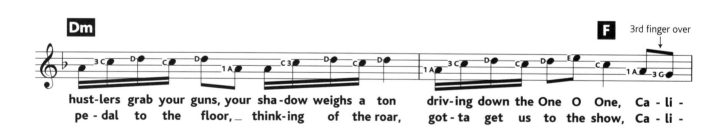

hust-lers grab your guns, your sha-dow weighs a ton driv-ing down the One O One, Ca - li -
pe - dal to the floor,_ think-ing of the roar, got - ta get us to the show, Ca - li -

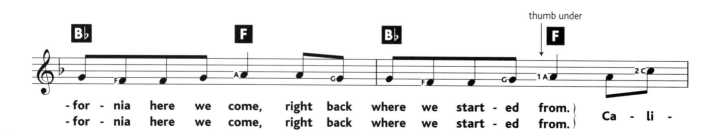

-for - nia here we come, right back where we start - ed from. Ca - li -
-for - nia here we come, right back where we start - ed from.

Words & Music by Alex Greenwald & Jason Schwartzman

© Copyright 2002 Beaucoup Bucks Music/Flying Saucer Fuel Music, USA.
Bug Music Limited.
All Rights Reserved. International Copyright Secured.

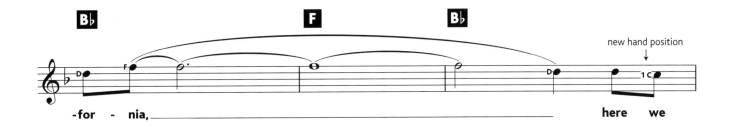

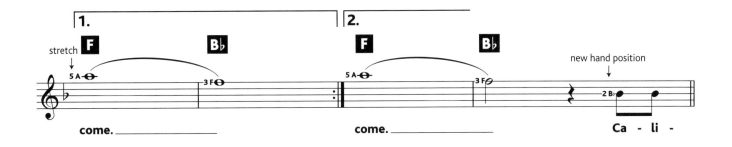

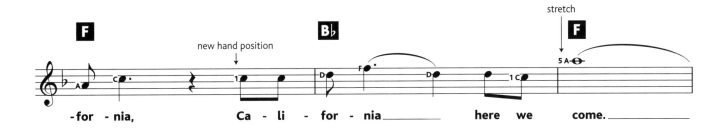

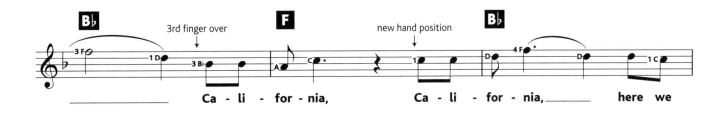

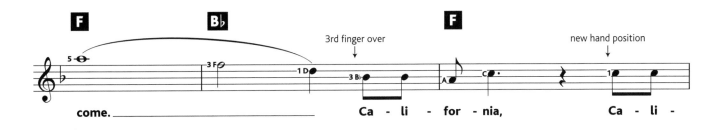

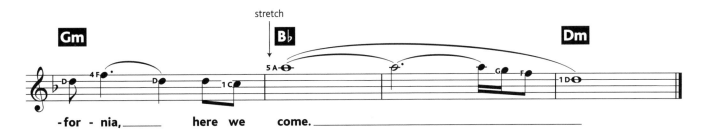

13

Don't Know Why

Norah Jones

Voice: **Guitar**
Rhythm: **Bossa nova**
Synchro start: **On**
Tempo: ♩ = 98

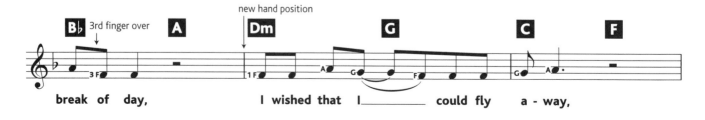

Words & Music by Jesse Harris
© Copyright 2002 Beanly Songs/Sony/ATV Songs LLC, USA.
Sony/ATV Music Publishing (UK) Limited.
All Rights Reserved. International Copyright Secured.

'stead of kneel - ing in the sand, catch-ing tear - drops

in my___ hand. My heart is drenched in____ wine.___

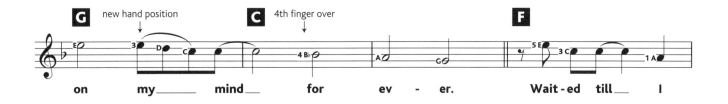

___ But you'll be

on my_____ mind___ for ev - er. Wait - ed till___ I

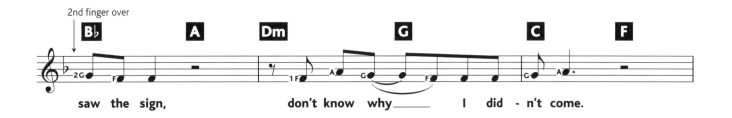

saw the sign, don't know why_____ I did - n't come.

I left you by___ the house of fun, don't know why_____ I did -

-n't come, I don't know why_ I did - n't come.

15

Everytime

Britney Spears

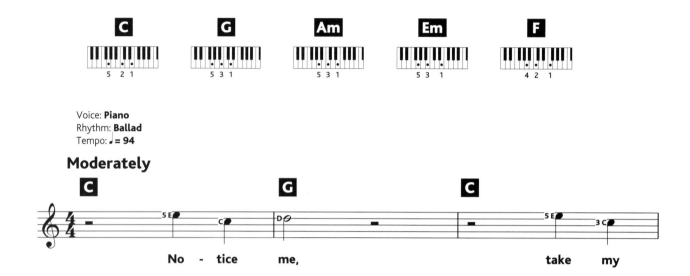

Voice: **Piano**
Rhythm: **Ballad**
Tempo: ♩ = 94

Moderately

No - tice me, take my

hand. Why are we

stran - gers when our love is

strong, why car - ry on with - out me?

Words & Music by Britney Spears & Annette Stamatelatos
© Copyright 2003 Zomba Music Publishers Limited/Copyright Control.
All Rights Reserved. International Copyright Secured.

Ev - 'ry time I try to fly ___ I fall, ___

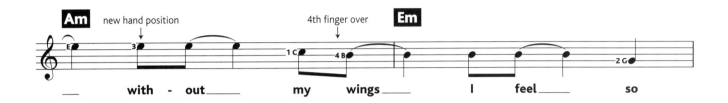

with - out ___ my wings ___ I feel ___ so

small. ___ I guess I need you ba - by.

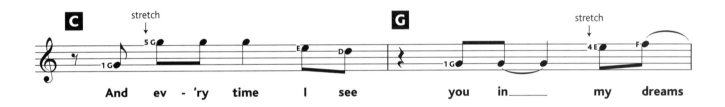

And ev - 'ry time I see you in ___ my dreams

___ I see ___ your face, ___ it's haunt - ing me. ___ I guess I

need you ba - by.   need you ba - by.

Feel

Robbie Williams

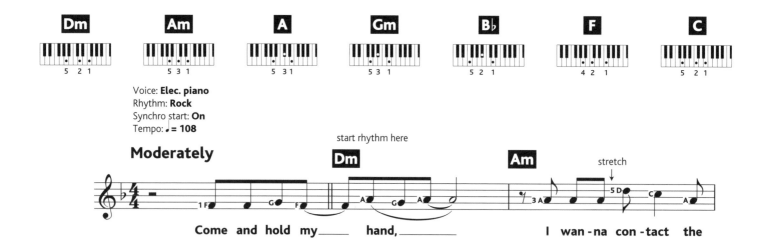

Voice: **Elec. piano**
Rhythm: **Rock**
Synchro start: **On**
Tempo: ♩ = 108

Moderately

start rhythm here

Come and hold my____ hand,____ I wan-na con-tact the

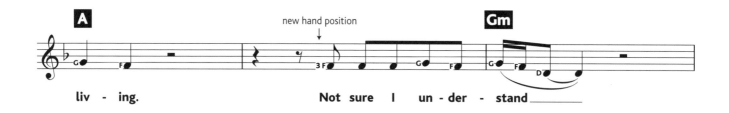

liv - ing. Not sure I un-der-stand____

new hand position

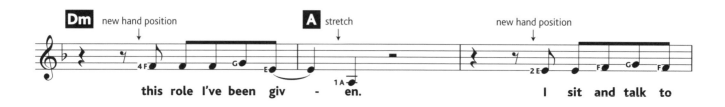

this role I've been giv - en. I sit and talk to

new hand position · stretch · new hand position

God,____ and he just laughs at my plans. _

new hand position · 2nd finger over

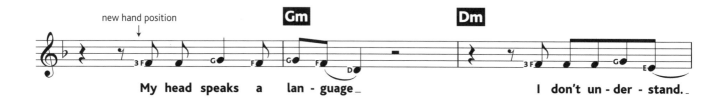

My head speaks a lan-guage _ I don't un-der-stand.

new hand position

Words & Music By Robbie Williams & Guy Chambers
© Copyright 2003 BMG Music Publishing Limited (50%)/
EMI Music Publishing Limited (50%).
All Rights Reserved. International Copyright Secured.

I just wan - na feel___ real___ love,_

feel the home that I live___ in. I got too much

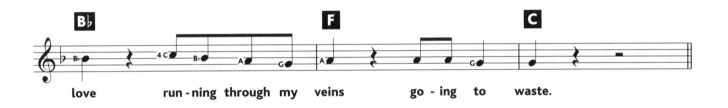

love run - ning through my veins go - ing to waste.

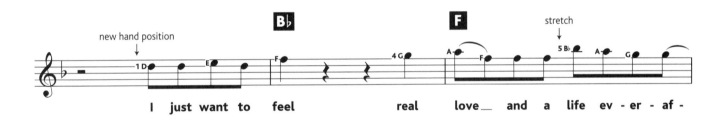

I just want to feel real love___ and a life ev - er - af -

- ter.___ There's a hole in my soul you can see it in my face,

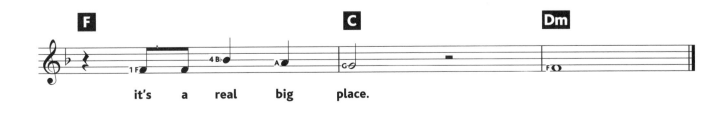

it's a real big place.

Gravity

Embrace

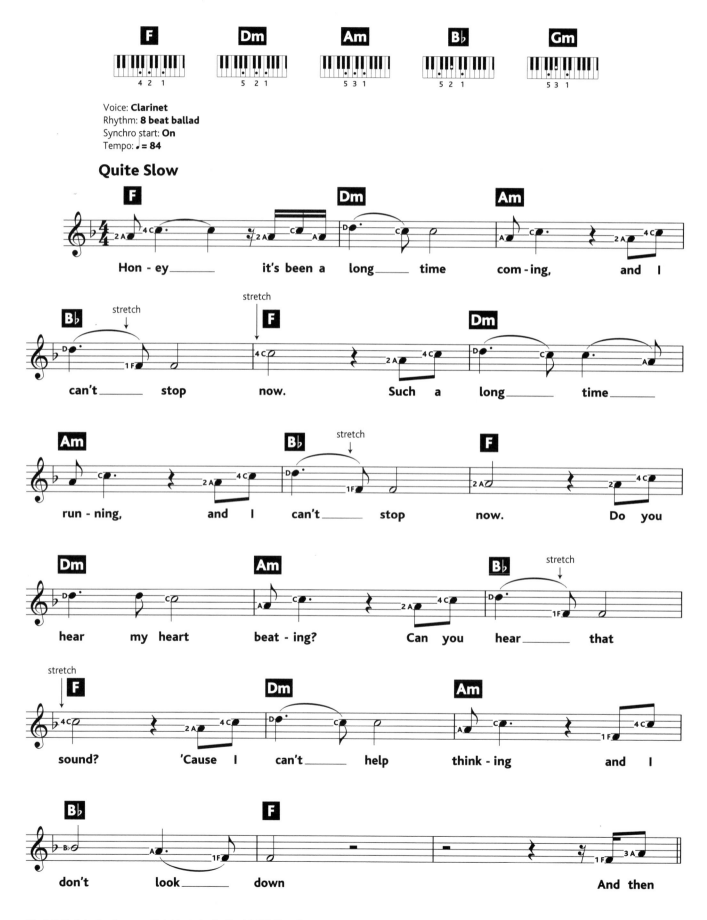

Voice: **Clarinet**
Rhythm: **8 beat ballad**
Synchro start: **On**
Tempo: ♩ = 84

Quite Slow

Words & Music by Guy Berryman, Chris Martin, Jon Buckland & Will Champion

© Copyright 2004 BMG Music Publishing Limited.
All Rights Reserved. International Copyright Secured.

I looked up at the sun and I could see oh the

way that gra-vi-ty turns for you and me._____ And then

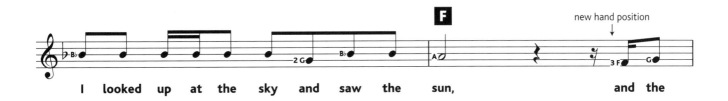

I looked up at the sky and saw the sun, and the

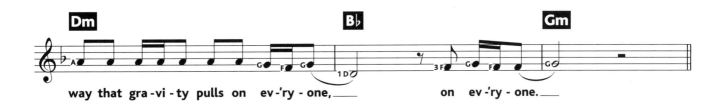

way that gra-vi-ty pulls on ev-'ry - one,_____ on ev-'ry - one._____

Can you hear my heart beat - ing? Can you

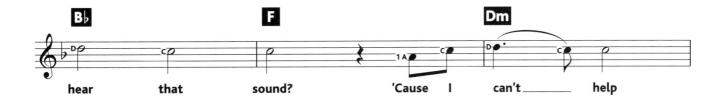

hear that sound? 'Cause I can't_____ help

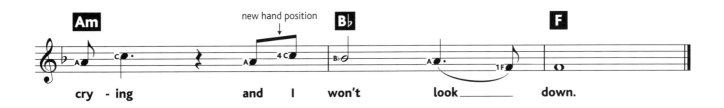

cry - ing and I won't look_____ down.

Heavy On My Heart

Anastacia

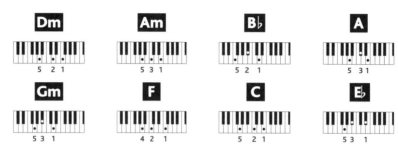

Voice: **Flute**
Rhythm: **Ballad**
Synchro start: **On**
Tempo: ♩ = **70**

Slowly

Try to fly a - way but it's im-pos - si - ble,_____ and ev - 'ry

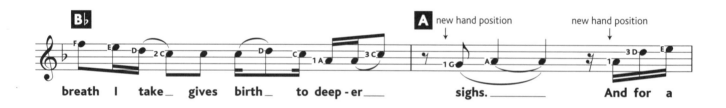

breath I take_ gives birth_ to deep - er____ sighs._____ And for a

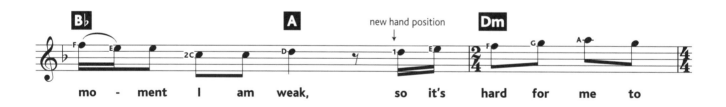

mo - ment I am weak, so it's hard for me to

speak, ev - en though we're un - der - neath the same blue

Words & Music by Billy Mann & Anastacia
© Copyright 2004 Universal/MCA Music Limited (50%)/
Sony/ATV Music Publishing Limited (50%).
All Rights Reserved. International Copyright Secured.

sky.

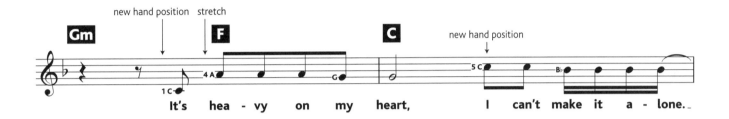

It's hea - vy on my heart, I can't make it a - lone.

Hea - vy on my heart, I can't find my way home.

Hea - vy on my heart, so come and

free me, it's so hea - vy on my heart.

Leave Right Now

Will Young

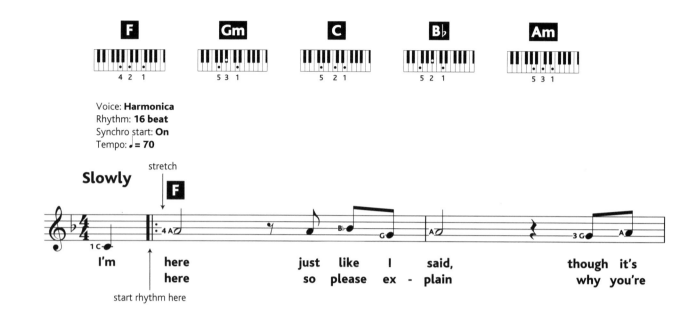

Voice: **Harmonica**
Rhythm: **16 beat**
Synchro start: **On**
Tempo: ♩ = 70

Slowly

stretch

start rhythm here

I'm here just like I said, though it's
here so please ex - plain why you're

break - ing ev - 'ry rule I've ev - er made. _____ My rac - ing
open - ing up a heal - ing wound a - gain. _____ I'm a lit - tle

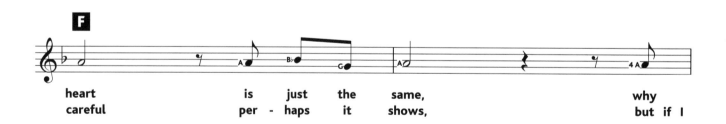

heart is just the same, why
careful per - haps it shows, but if I

make it strong to break it once a - gain. _____
lose the highs at least I'm spared the lows. _____

Words & Music by Francis White

© Copyright 2003 Universal Music Publishing Limited.
All Rights Reserved. International Copyright Secured.

And I'd love to say I do, give ev - 'ry - thing to
Now I trem - ble in your arms, what could be the

you, but I can nev - er now be true.
harm to feel my spi - rit come. So I say,

Think I bet - ter leave right now, be - fore I fall a - ny deep - er,

think I bet - ter leave right now, feel - ing weak - er and weak - er.

Some - bo - dy bet - ter show me how, be - fore I fall an - y deep - er,

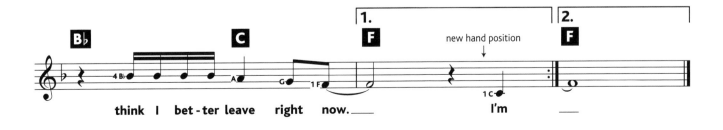

think I bet - ter leave right now. I'm

Somewhere Only We Know

Keane

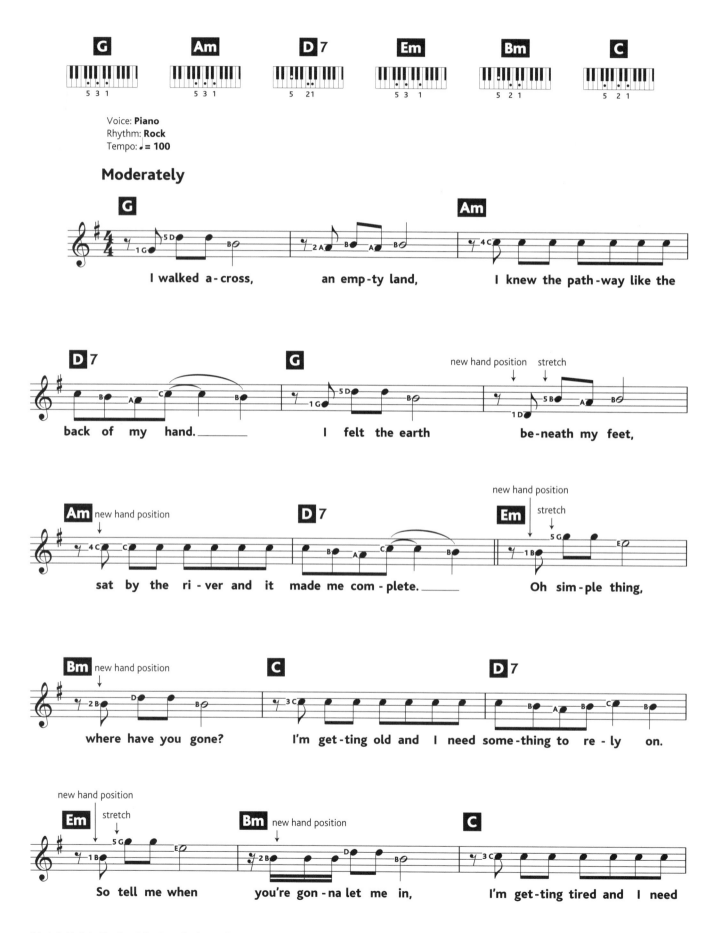

Voice: **Piano**
Rhythm: **Rock**
Tempo: ♩ = 100

Moderately

I walked a-cross, an emp-ty land, I knew the path-way like the back of my hand. I felt the earth be-neath my feet, sat by the ri-ver and it made me com-plete. Oh sim-ple thing, where have you gone? I'm get-ting old and I need some-thing to re-ly on. So tell me when you're gon-na let me in, I'm get-ting tired and I need

Words & Music by Tim Rice-Oxley, Tom Chaplin & Richard Hughes
© Copyright 2004 BMG Music Publishing Limited.
All Rights Reserved. International Copyright Secured.

some -where to be - gin._____ I came a - cross a fall - en tree,

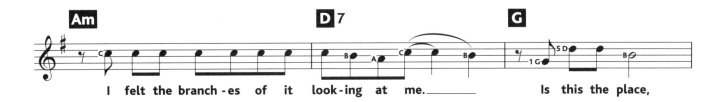

I felt the branch -es of it look -ing at me._____ Is this the place,

we used to love? Is this the place that I've been dream - ing of?_____

Oh sim -ple thing, where have you gone? I'm get -ting old and I need

some -thing to re -ly on. So tell me when you're gon - na let me in,

I'm get - ting tired and I need some -where to be - gin._____

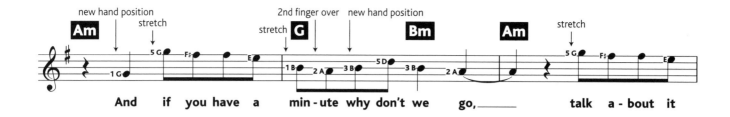

And if you have a min-ute why don't we go,_____ talk a-bout it

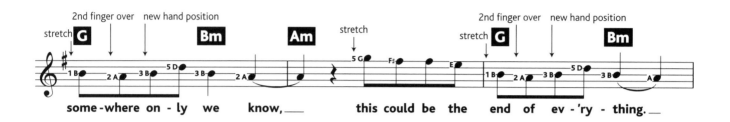

some-where on-ly we know,___ this could be the end of ev-'ry-thing.__

So who don't we___ go some-where on-ly we know.

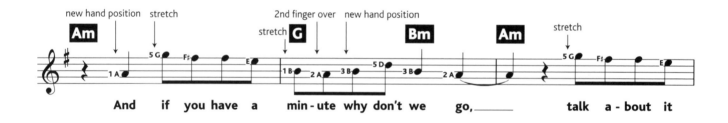

And if you have a min-ute why don't we go,_____ talk a-bout it

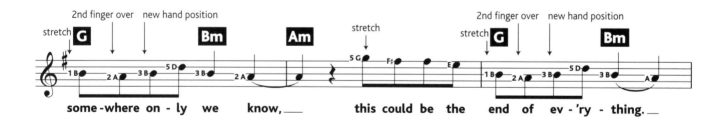

some-where on-ly we know,___ this could be the end of ev-'ry-thing.__

So who don't we___ go some-where on-ly we know.___

Mad World

Michael Andrews feat. Gary Jules

Voice: **Piano**
Rhythm: **8 beat ballad**
Tempo: ♩ = **84**

Slowly

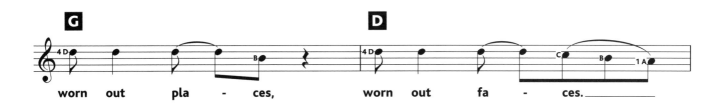

All a - round me are fa - mi - liar fa - ces,

worn out pla - ces, worn out fa - ces.

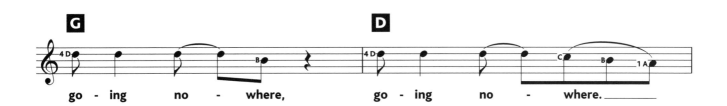

Bright and ear - ly for their dai - ly ra - ces,

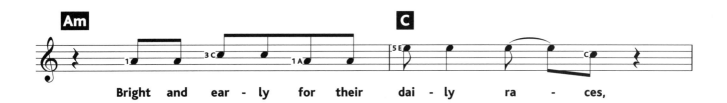

go - ing no - where, go - ing no - where.

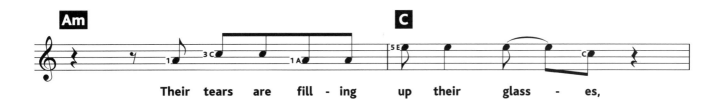

Their tears are fill - ing up their glass - es,

Words & Music by Roland Orzabal
© Copyright 1982 Roland Orzabal Limited.
Chrysalis Music Limited.
All Rights Reserved. International Copyright Secured.

no ex - pres - sion,   no ex - pres - sion. _____

Hide my head, I wan - na drown my sor - row,

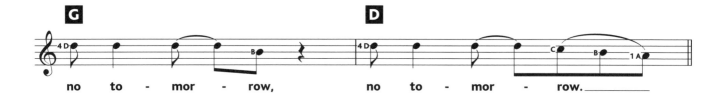

no to - mor - row,   no to - mor - row. _____

And I find it kind - a fun - ny, I find it kind - a

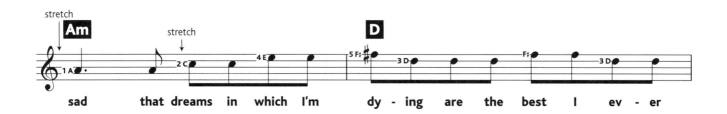

sad that dreams in which I'm dy - ing are the best I ev - er

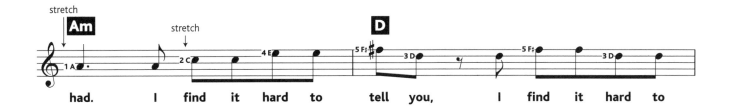

had.   I   find   it   hard   to   tell   you,   I   find   it   hard   to

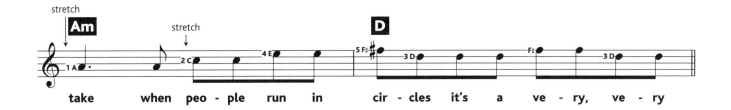

take   when   peo - ple   run   in   cir - cles   it's   a   ve - ry,   ve - ry

mad   world.   Mad   world.

En - larg - en   your   world.   Mad

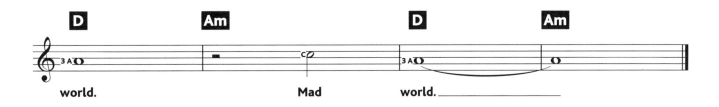

world.   Mad   world._____

Sometimes You Can't Make It On Your Own

U2

Voice: **Guitar**
Rhythm: **Ballad**
Synchro start: **On**
Tempo: ♩ = 90

Quite Slow

Tough, you think you've got the stuff.

You're tell - ing me___ and a - ny - one___ you're

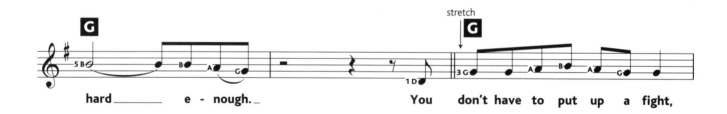

hard___ e - nough. ___ You don't have to put up a fight,

you don't have to al - ways be___ right.

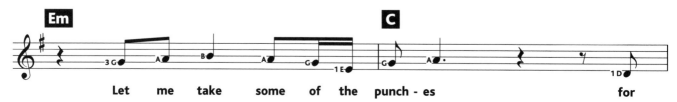

Let me take some of the punch - es for

Words by Bono. Music by U2.
© Copyright 2004 Blue Mountain Music Limited/Mother Music/
Universal International Music Publishing B.V.
All Rights Reserved. International Copyright Secured.

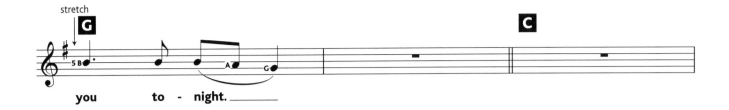

you   to - night.

Lis - ten   to   me   now,   need   to   let____   you

know, __   you   don't   have   to   go   it   a - lone. _____

__   And   it's   you   when   I   look   in   the   mir -

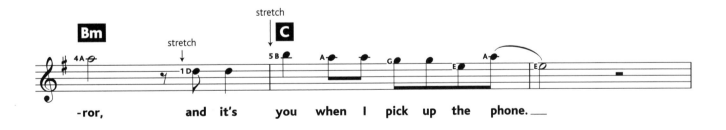

-ror,   and   it's   you   when   I   pick   up   the   phone. __

Some - times   you   can't   make   it   on   your   own. _____

This Love

Maroon 5

Voice: **Elec guitar**
Rhythm: **Funk**
Tempo: ♩ = **94**

Moderately

I was so high I did not re - cog - nise___ the fire burn - ing

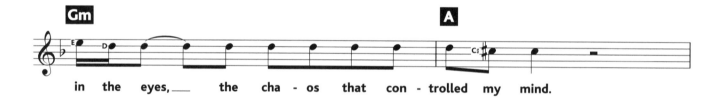

in the eyes,___ the cha - os that con - trolled my mind.

Whis - pered good - bye as she got on a plane,___ nev - er to re -

stretch

-turn a - gain,___ but al - ways in my heart. Oh!

Words & Music by Adam Levine, James Valentine, Jesse Carmichael, Mickey Madden & Ryan Dusick

© Copyright 2002 BMG Music Publishing Limited.
All Rights Reserved. International Copyright Secured.

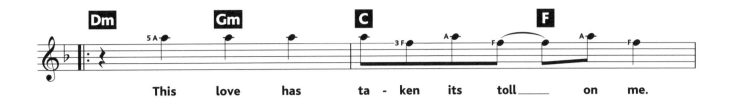

This love has ta - ken its toll____ on me.

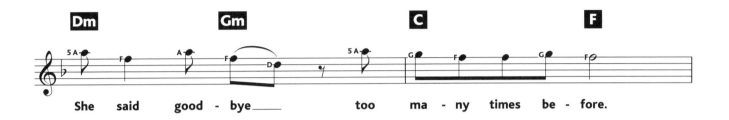

She said good - bye____ too ma - ny times be - fore.

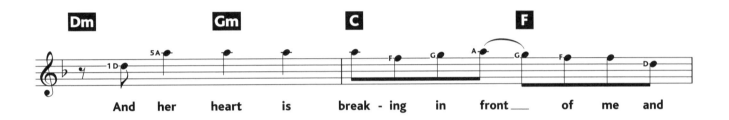

And her heart is break - ing in front____ of me and

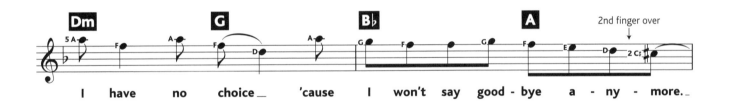

I have no choice____ 'cause I won't say good - bye a - ny - more.____

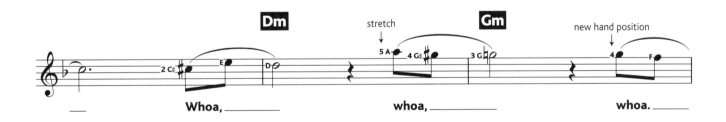

____ Whoa,_____ whoa,_____ whoa.____

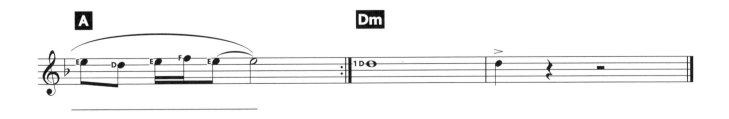

Wires

Athlete

Voice: **Guitar**
Rhythm: **Ballad**
Synchro start: **On**
Tempo: ♩ = **70**

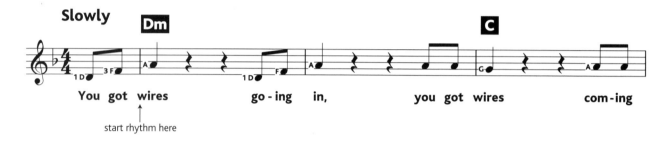

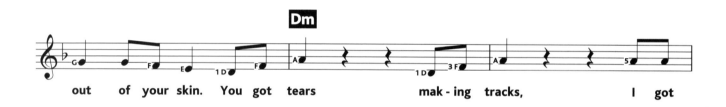

Words & Music by Joel Pott, Carey Willetts, Steve Roberts & Tim Wanstall
© Copyright 2003 Chrysalis Music Limited
All Rights Reserved. International Copyright Secured.

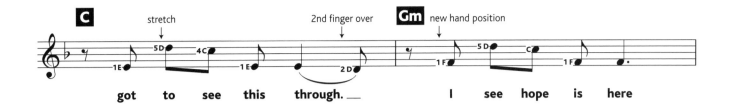

got to see this through. ___ I see hope is here

in a plas - tic box. I've seen Christ - mas lights

ref - lect in your eyes. I see it in your ___

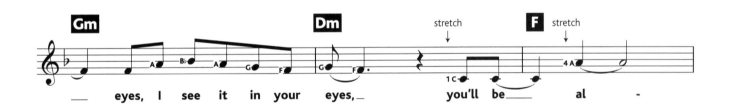

___ eyes, I see it in your eyes, ___ you'll be___ al -

-right. I see it in your ___ eyes, I see it in your eyes, ___ you'll be___

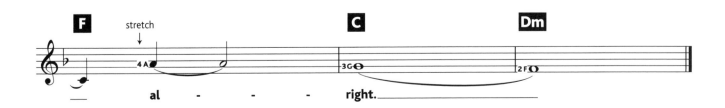

___ al - - - right._____

The Scientist

Coldplay

Voice: **Clarinet**
Rhythm: **8 beat ballad**
Tempo: ♩ = 84

Quite Slow

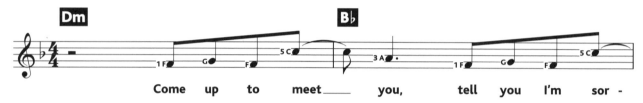

Come up to meet___ you, tell you I'm sor -

- ry, you don't know how love - ly you are.___

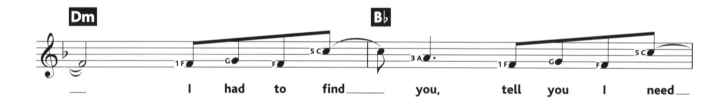

___ I had to find___ you, tell you I need___

___ you, tell you I'll set___ you a - part.___

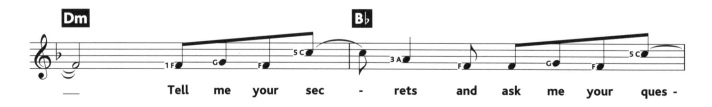

Tell me your sec - rets and ask me your ques -

Words & Music by Guy Berryman, Chris Martin, Jon Buckland & Will Champion
© Copyright 2002 BMG Music Publishing Limited.
All Rights Reserved. International Copyright Secured.

- tions,   oh let's go   back_____ to   the   start._____

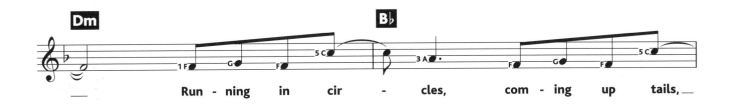

___   Run - ning   in   cir   - cles,   com - ing   up   tails, ___

_____   heads   on   a   si   -   lence   a - part._____

new hand position

No - bo - dy   said   it   was   ea   - sy, ___

new hand position   3rd finger over

it's   such   a   shame___   for   us   to   part._____

39

No - bo - dy said it was ea - sy,

no - one ev - er said it would be this hard.

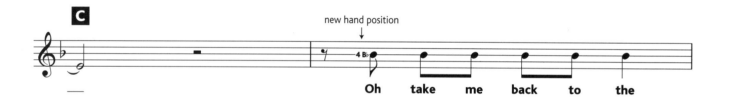

Oh take me back to the

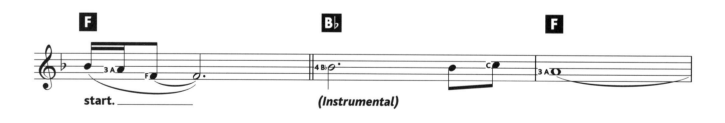

start. (Instrumental)

1 2 3 4 5 6 7 8 9